PJMASKS

Battle of the HQs

"Greg. Connor. Do you read me?"
Amaya held the walkie-talkie up to her ear.
"We hear you loud and clear!" replied Connor.
"Me too," said Greg. "Over."
Amaya grinned. Before she could speak again,
a light shone into her bedroom.

"It's a school bus . . . with a Ninjalino driving it!"
gasped Amaya.
The Ninjalino was not alone. Bus after bus chugged
down the street, each with its own purple driver.

What was going on? Amaya, Connor
and Greg had to find out!

PJ MASKS ARE ON THEIR WAY, INTO THE NIGHT TO SAVE THE DAY!

NIGHT IN THE CITY. A BRAVE BAND OF HEROES IS READY TO FACE FIENDISH VILLAINS TO STOP THEM MESSING WITH YOUR DAY.

AMAYA BECOMES . . . **OWLETTE!**

CONNOR BECOMES . . .

CATBOY!

GREG BECOMES ... **GEKKO!**

It didn't take the PJ Masks
long to track down the stolen buses.
The Ninjalinos had piled them up into a
tower, right in front of their own HQ! Night
Ninja was standing at the top.
"Isn't it a lovely night to park . . .
in the park?" he jeered.

"Mwa ha ha ha!"

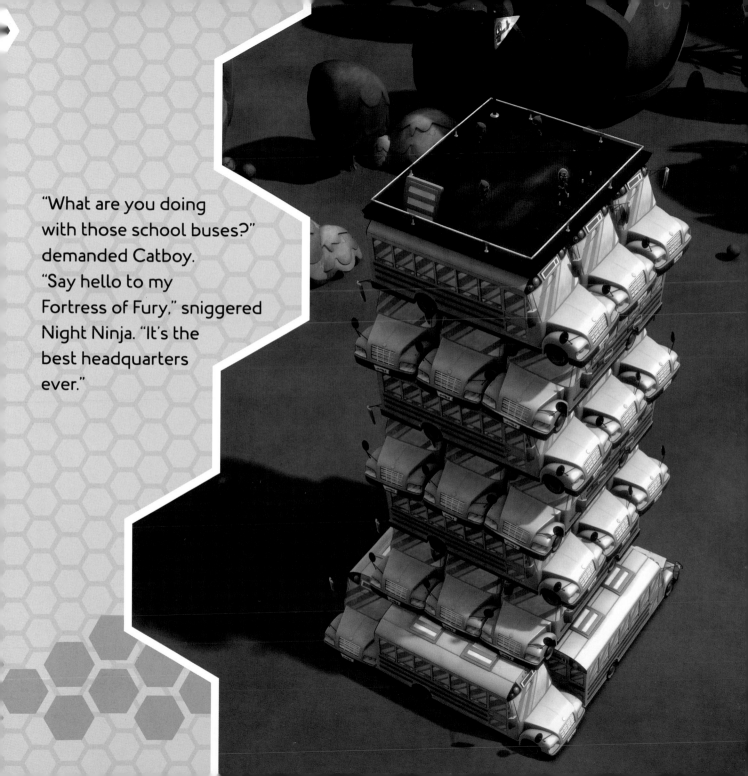

"What are you doing with those school buses?" demanded Catboy.
"Say hello to my Fortress of Fury," sniggered Night Ninja. "It's the best headquarters ever."

"Put those buses back," shouted Gekko.
"Make me!" replied Night Ninja.
Owlette decided to fly up and get a
closer look at the Fortress of Fury.
"Super Owl Wings!"

Night Ninja was ready for Owlette.
"Let's give the noisy bird girl a nice loud greeting," he chuckled.
When the villain gave his order, all of the Ninjalinos slammed
on their bus horns.

"HOOOONKK!"

The sound was deafening.
It blasted Owlette out
of the sky!

Catboy caught Owlette just in time.
"That horn defence is good," she gasped. "We should
get it for our HQ."
Catboy shook his head. Their base already had loads of
cool stuff that could stop Night Ninja – they didn't need
any of his tricks!

But Owlette wasn't listening. While Catboy and Gekko got
into their super vehicles, she rushed back to HQ.
"Listen to this noise, Night Ninja," she said, pressing a button
on the PJ Picture Player. "It's the Cat's Meow!"
The Cat's Meow was noisy –
noisy enough to send
Catboy's car into a spin!

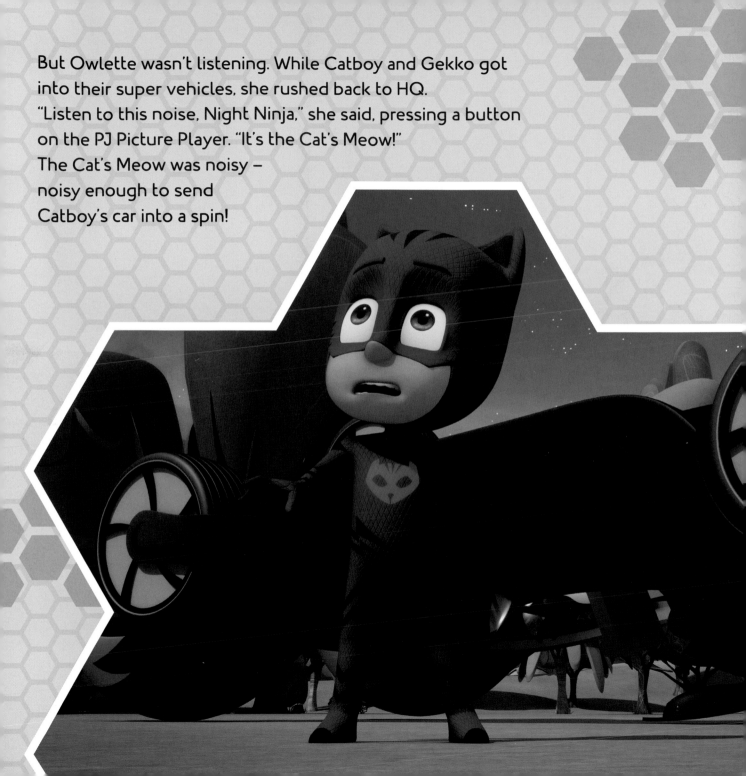

With Catboy out of action, Gekko was on his own.
He drove on towards the stack of school buses.
"Let him have it, Ninjalinos!" bellowed Night Ninja.
A shower of sticky splats pelted the Gekko-Mobile.
It was stuck fast in seconds! Gekko had to get out and run.

The Fortress of Fury has sticky splat catapults. We need those things, too.

Owlette needed to help her friends, but she had other things on her mind.

"Super Gekko Camouflage!"

Gekko made himself invisible so he could climb up the side of the bus tower. At the same time, Owlette started firing furballs at Night Ninja's base! One bounced off Gekko, giving away his hiding place. "Owlette!" groaned Gekko. "We're on the same team."

Night Ninja spotted Gekko at once. "There you are!"
The Fortress of Fury began to spin round and round. Gekko was
flung to the ground.
"Fluttering feathers!" gasped Owlette. "His fortress can spin, too?"

Night Ninja was starting to enjoy himself. "I hope that you're not tired of this battle, PJ Masks," he called. "Because you're about to get really tyred."

Every bus window in the villain's fortress opened at the same time. There was a Ninjalino inside each one, sitting on a bus tyre.

"Fire the tyres!" shouted Night Ninja. Hundreds of Ninjalinos soared through the air, straight towards the PJ Masks' HQ!

The tyres didn't hit the PJ Masks' base, they landed in the moat instead.

"Why is Night Ninja filling the moat with tyres?" asked Catboy.

"To make a bridge," replied Gekko. "He is bringing his fortress over to destroy our base!"

Catboy helped Gekko get down to the moat.
While they tried to break up the bridge together,
Owlette was busy at the control board.
"Now we're spinning!" she cried.
The PJ Masks' HQ turned round and round. Tyres
bounced off its walls, then landed on top of Gekko!

The extra tyres had made the Night Ninja's bridge even stronger. "This is my fault," said Owlette. "The Fortress of Fury has all these new things and I wanted them, too. I'm sorry. We don't need new things just because someone else has them."

Catboy and Gekko looked out at Night Ninja.
He was no match for the PJ Masks!
"Don't worry," said Catboy. "We'll get the
school buses back."
"It's time to be a hero,"
agreed Owlette.

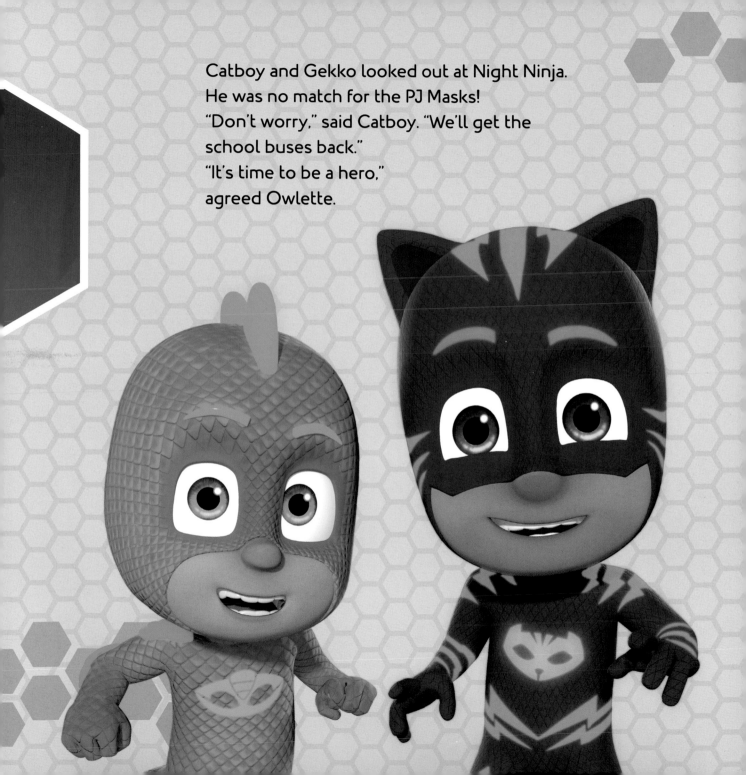

The PJ Masks worked together to get the job done.

"Let's go!" said Owlette.

The heroes each fired a giant furball at the bottom of Night Ninja's tower.

One, two . . . three! The Fortress of Fury began to wobble.

"Nice shot, Catboy," said Gekko.

The baddie's base was falling over. Gekko used his muscles to catch the tumbling buses.
"How do you like that, Night Ninja?" asked Catboy.
"Noooo!" shouted the villain.
Night Ninja did not like it at all!

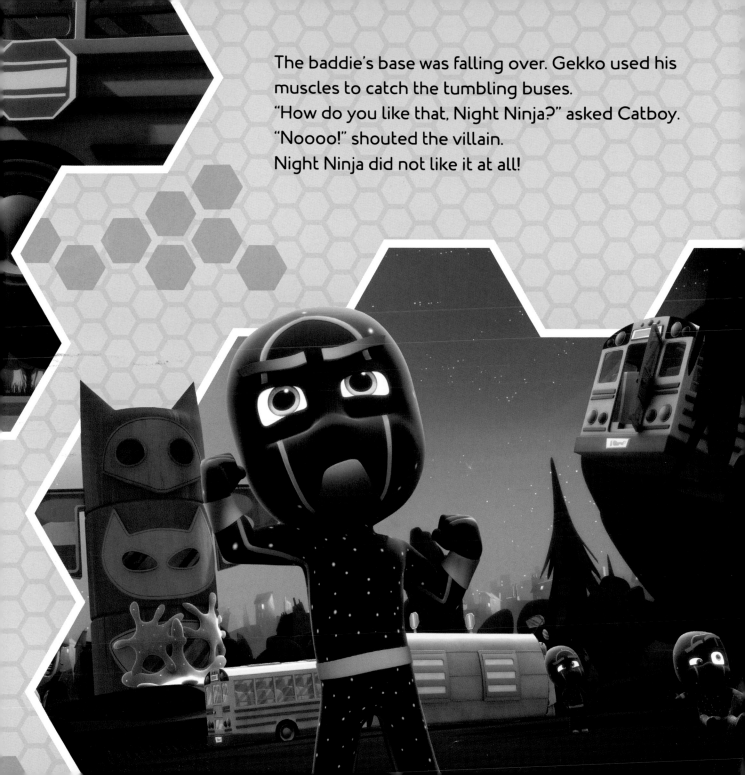

Night Ninja ran away, followed by his naughty Ninjalinos.
Gekko punched the air. "Yes!"
"Good job!" cried Catboy.
"Awesome!" agreed Owlette.
The PJ Masks had won the battle of the bases!

PJ MASKS ALL SHOUT HOORAY.
'CAUSE IN THE NIGHT, WE SAVED THE DAY!